ACTIVITY BOOK

My name is _____ .

How are you, Tiger? — page ③

1 A Surprise — page ⑤

2 A New Pet — page ⑬

Tiger Review 1 — page ㉑

3 Where's my coat? — page ㉓

4 Break Time — page ㉛

Tiger Review 2 — page ㊴

5 What's the matter? — page ㊶

6 On Holiday — page ㊾

Tiger Review 3 — page ㊼

Halloween — page ㊾

Christmas — page 60

Carnival — page 61

CLIL Picture Dictionary — page 62

Carol Read • Mark Ormerod

Macmillan Education Limited
4 Crinan Street
London N1 9XW

Companies and representatives throughout the world

ISBN 978 0 230 47630 1

Designed by Blooberry Design Ltd
Illustrated by Adrian Barclay, Simon Walmesley and Rodrigo Folgueira
Cover design by Astwood Design Consultancy
Cover illustration by Rodrigo Folgueira
Author photograph (Carol Read) by Michael Shelley
Songs produced and arranged by Tom, Dick and Debbie Productions

Authors' acknowledgments

We would like to thank everyone at Macmillan Education in the UK and in Spain who has helped us in the development and the production of these materials. We would also like to thank all the teachers who have taken time to read, pilot and give feedback at every stage of writing the course. Special thanks from Carol to Alan, Jamie and Hannah for their encouragement and support. Special thanks from Mark to Carlos for his patience and understanding.

Acknowledgments

The publishers would also like to thank the following teachers:

Ana I. Martín Sierra, CEIP San Sebastián, San Sebastián de los Reyes, Madrid; Ana Mª Muñoz Jacinto, CEIP El Algarrobillo, Valencina de la Concepción, Sevilla; Ángel Martínez Tofé, CEIP Escultor Vicente Ochoa, Logroño, La Rioja; Anna Lorente Clemente, Escola Miquel Martí i Pol, Sant Feliu de Llobregat, Barcelona; Bibiana Comas Planàs, Escola Mallorca, Barcelona; Juana María Torres Medina, CEIP Virgen de Valderrabé, Algete, Madrid; Julia Selma Monedero, CEIP José García Planells, Manises, Valencia; Julie-Ann Eckroth Engelter, CEIP El Tejar, Majadahonda, Madrid; María Ques Jordà, CEIP Son Oliva, Palma de Mallorca, Baleares; Mª Cruz Corrales Fernández, CEIP Santísimo Cristo de la Salud, Hervás, Cáceres; Maripi Arriaga Aznar, CEIP Gerbert d'Orlhac, Sant Cugat del Vallès, Barcelona; Marta Civera Sanfélix, Colegio Sagrado Corazón, Mislata, Valencia; Rafael Aguayo Villamor, Landauri Ikastola, Vitoria-Gasteiz, Álava; Sandra Freire Molina, Colegio La Purísima, Orense; Silvia Cebollada Soriano, CEIP El Tejar, Majadahonda, Madrid; Sylvia Frei Salcedo, CEIP La Cañada, Olías, Málaga.

Printed and bound in Uruguay

2020

25

How are you, Tiger?

1 ✏️ 💬 **Read, complete and act out.** ✏️ **Colour Tiger.**

> Hello   fine   play   ~~Tiger~~   you

1 Hello, *Tiger*.

2 Hello, Sue. _____, Jay.

3 How are _____?

4 I'm _____. Thank you.

5 Come on. Let's _____.

2 ✏️ **Write about the characters. Write about you.**

1 I'm *Sue*. I'm *nine*.

2 I'm _____. I'm _____.

3 _____ _____

4 _____ _____

3 ✏️ **Count and write.** 🖍️ **Read and colour the crayons.**

crayons   trees   ~~ice creams~~

_15_   _ice creams_

——— ——————   ——— ——————

4 ✏️ **Complete.** 🖍️ **Colour your favourite day.**

T F ~~M~~ S S T W

Monday   ___uesday   ___ednesday

___hursday   ___riday   ___aturday   ___unday

1 A Surprise

Vocabulary

1 🖊 **Read, look and number.** 💬 **Say.**

It's the bathroom. `2`

It's the living room. ☐

It's the dining room. ☐

It's the kitchen. ☐

It's the garage. ☐

It's the toilet. ☐

It's the bedroom. ☐

It's the hall. ☐

Number 1. What is it?

It's the bedroom.

2 **Count the tigers in the picture.** 🖊 **Write the number.**

 = ☐

Vocabulary and story

3 ✏️ **Look and write.**

   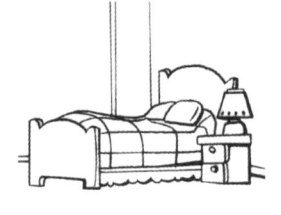

ha _l_ _l_ b_ _ _ _ _ _ _ L_ _ _ _ _ _ b_ _ _ _ _
_ _ _ _

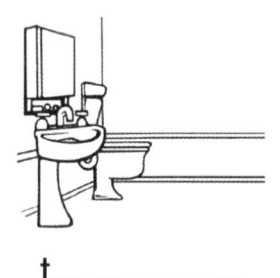   

t_ _ _ _ _ k_ _ _ _ _ _ _ d_ _ _ _ _ _ g_ _ _ _ _
_ _ _ _

4 ✏️ **Find and circle Li, Jay and Tiger. Write the room.**

Li is in the
bedroom .

Jay is in the
_____.

Tiger is in the
_____.

What do you think?

✏️ **Colour.**

The story is …

 OK.

 good.

 great!

Story activity and vocabulary production: writing

Song

5 🖉 **Look and write.** **Listen and check.** 🎵 **Sing** *Where's Li?*

Where's Li?

Where can she be?

Is she in the _h a l l_  ?

Is she next to the _ _ _ _ _ _  ?

Is she in the _ _ _ _ _ _  ?

Is she behind the _ _ _ _ _  ?

Is she in the _ _ _ _ _ _ _  ?

Is she under the _ _ _ _ _ _ 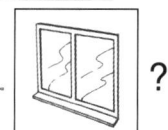 ?

Li is in the _ _ _ _ _ _ _  .

She's in the bedroom, in a cupboard with Tiger!

Language and communication

6 ✏️✏️ **Read, write and colour the answer.**

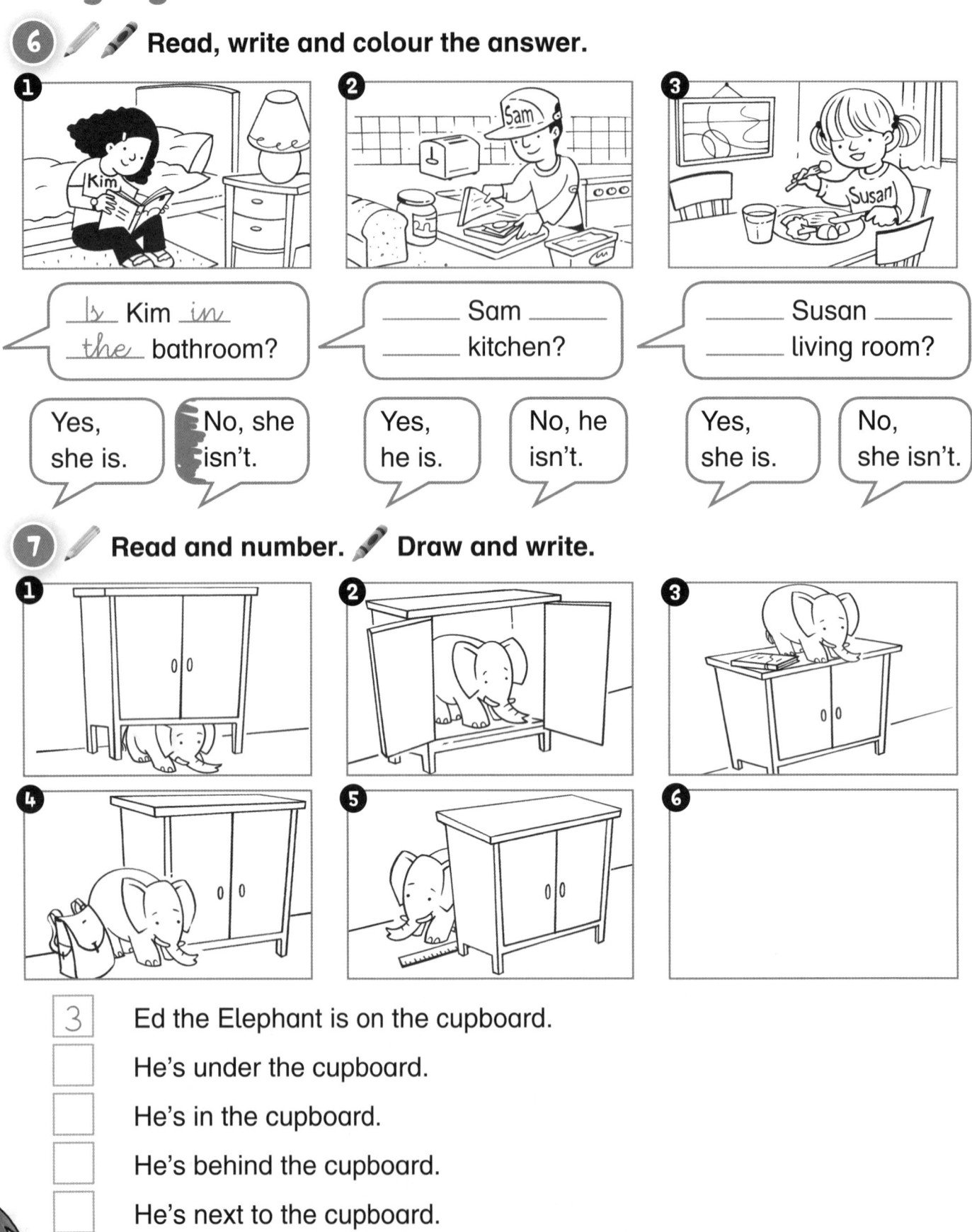

1 Is Kim in the bathroom?

Yes, she is. | No, she isn't.

2 _____ Sam _____ kitchen?

Yes, he is. | No, he isn't.

3 _____ Susan _____ living room?

Yes, she is. | No, she isn't.

7 ✏️ **Read and number.** ✏️ **Draw and write.**

3	Ed the Elephant is on the cupboard.
	He's under the cupboard.
	He's in the cupboard.
	He's behind the cupboard.
	He's next to the cupboard.
6	_____

Completing the sentences: writing

CLIL: Things in our homes

8 ✏️ **Look and find. Write.**

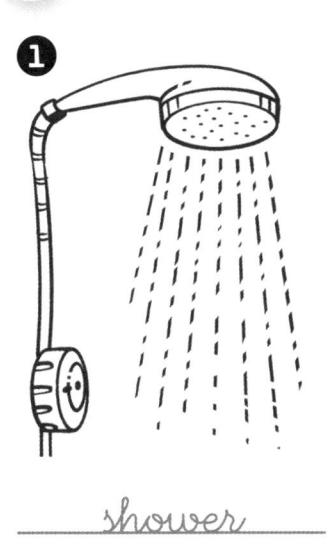

V	G	K	A	L	C	L	O	C	K
O	P	S	Y	T	O	E	R	B	N
L	T	H	I	I	O	B	D	F	S
Q	U	O	R	E	K	B	V	X	Z
S	J	W	A	B	E	D	O	U	L
O	I	E	N	H	R	D	O	P	N
F	B	R	H	E	E	T	U	C	I
A	O	N	S	F	R	I	D	G	E

1 *shower*

2

3

4

5

6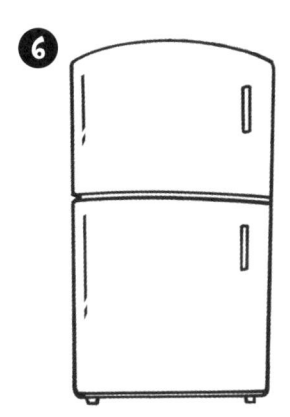

9 🖍️ **Read and colour the objects in Activity 8.**

> The sofa is purple.
>
> The fridge is blue.
>
> The clock is orange and brown.
>
> The bed is green and yellow.
>
> The cooker is red and black.
>
> The shower is grey, black and white.

Learning about content: reading and writing

CLIL: Things in our homes

 10 ✏ **Find, circle and write.** 🔘 🎵 **Sing *The shower is in the bathroom.***

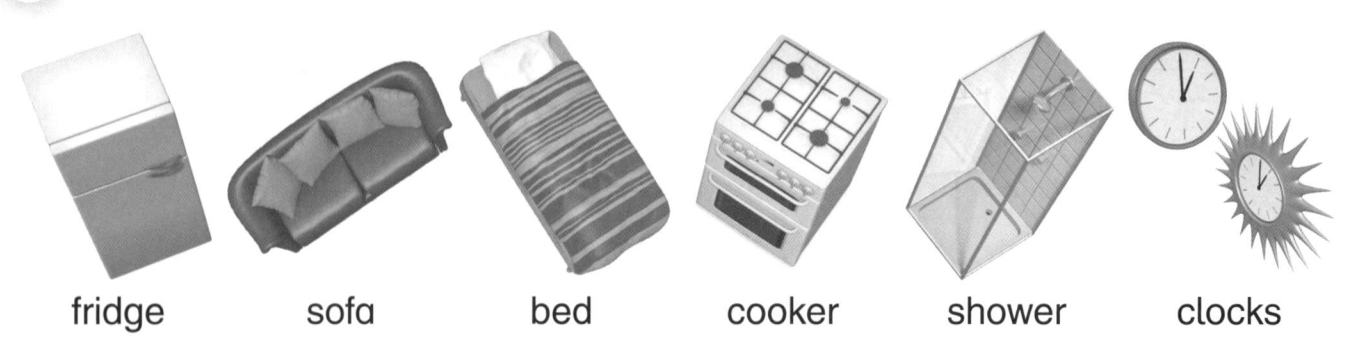

fridge   sofa   bed   cooker   shower   clocks

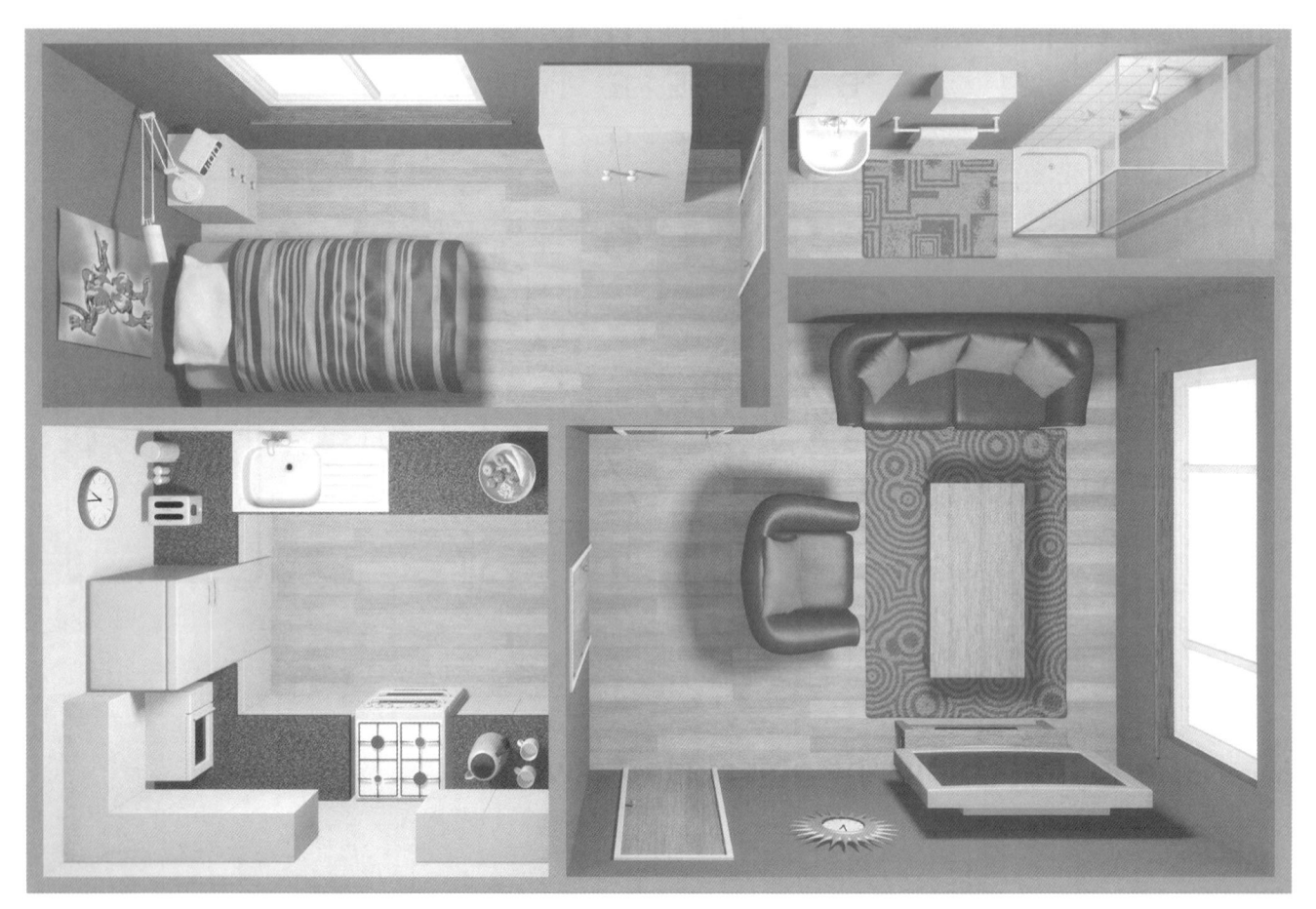

1 The ___cooker___ is in the kitchen.

2 The _____ is in the bedroom.

3 The _____ is in the bathroom.

4 The _____ is in the kitchen.

5 The _____ is in the living room.

6 And _____ are in many rooms.

Learning about content: writing

11. ✎ **Label the pictures. Complete the sentences.**

bed

1

The _____*bed*_____ is

in the _____*bedroom*_____.

2

The _____ is

in the _____.

3

The _____ is

in the _____.

4

The _____ is

in the _____.

12. ✎ **Tick (✔) what you can do.**

kitchen

1 2

kitchen
bedroom

3

4

sofa
cooker
shower

sofa

Revision and self-assessment

Key for Activity 12: I can 1) say the names of rooms, 2) read and write the names of rooms, 3) understand the story, 4) read and write the names of things in our homes.

11

Kids' Culture 1

1 ✏️ **Read and write.** 🔊 CD1 27 💬 **Listen and say the rhyme.**

box   room   cupboard   ~~house~~   room   box   cupboard

In a dark, dark _house_

is a dark, dark _____.

In the dark, dark _____

is a dark, dark _____.

In the dark, dark _____

is a dark, dark _____.

In the dark, dark _____

is a … SURPRISE!

2 ✏️ **Read and match.**

❶ I live in a flat.

❷ I live in a houseboat.

❸ I live in a house.

ⓐ   ⓑ   ⓒ

Intercultural learning: reading and writing

2 A New Pet

Vocabulary

1 🖊 **Read, look and number.** 💬 **Say.**

It's a bird. `6`

It's a kitten.

It's a fish.

It's a hamster.

It's a lizard.

It's a puppy.

It's a rabbit.

It's a turtle.

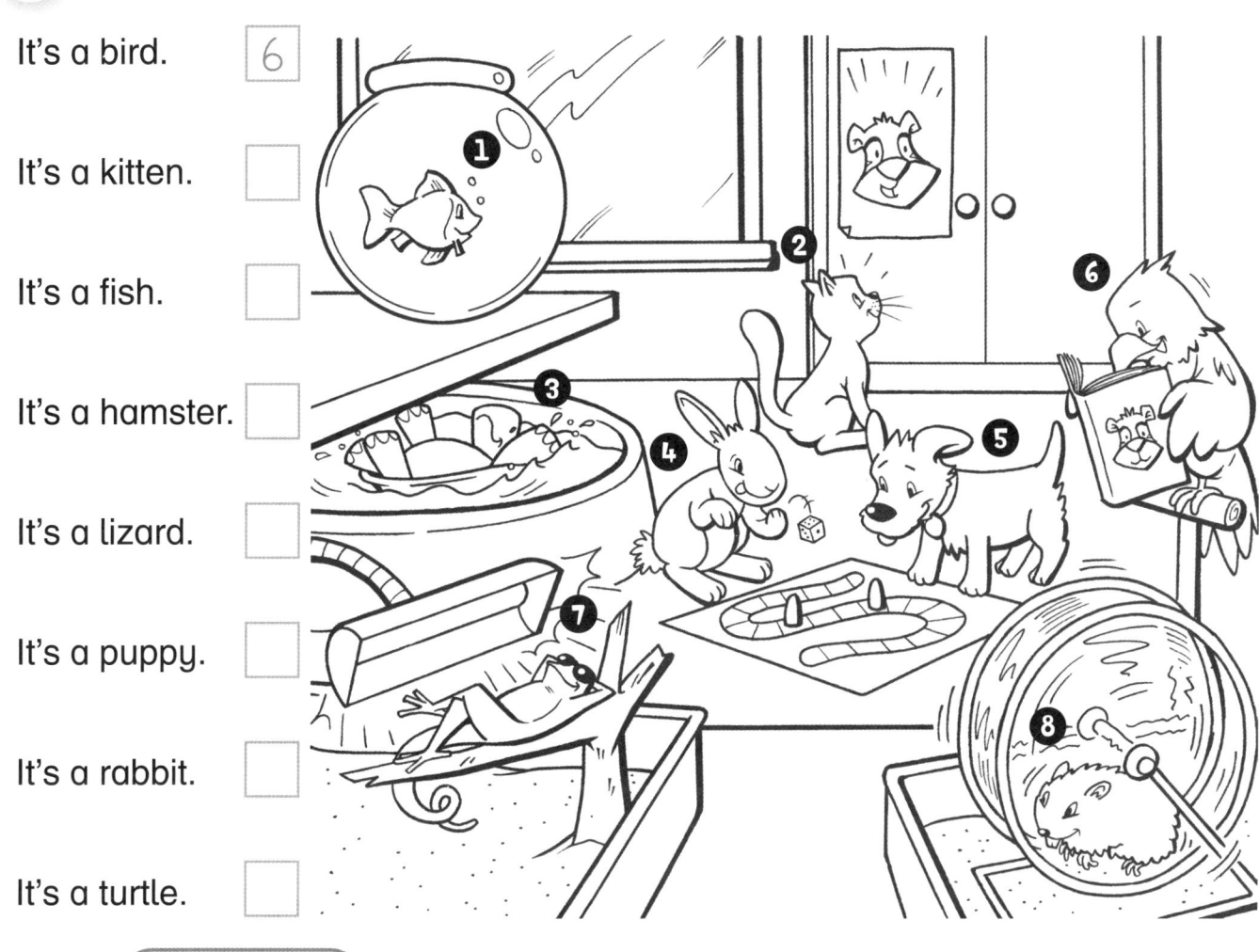

Number 1.
What is it?

It's a fish.

2 **Count the tigers.** 🖊 **Write the number.**

 =

Vocabulary and story

3 Tick (✔) the animals in the story.

bird ☐	kitten ☐	fish ☐	hamster ☐
lizard ☐	puppy ☐	rabbit ☐	turtle ☐

4 Colour Li's new pet. Complete the sentence.

Li hasn't got a kitten.
She hasn't got a rabbit.

Li has got a

_____ .

What do you think?

Colour.

The story is …

OK. good. great!

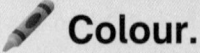

Story activity and vocabulary production: writing

Song

5 ✏ **Look and write.** 🔘 CD1 35 **Listen and check.** 🎵 **Sing *She's got a new pet.***

Look! Li has got a new pet.

Has she got a _____hamster_____ 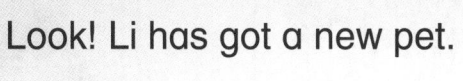 ?

What has she got?

Has she got a _____  ?

Or … is it a rock?

Has she got a _____  ?

What has she got?

Has she got a _____  ?

Or … is it a rock?

Li has got a _____  !

Well, well, well!

She's got a _____

with a beautiful shell!

Language and communication

6 🖊️🖍️ **Read, write and colour the answer.**

 **MARY**

 **JOE**

 **KATE**

Has Mary _got_ _a_ fish?

_____ Joe _____ hamster?

_____ Kate _____ puppy?

Yes, she has.

Yes, he has.

Yes, she has.

No, she hasn't.

No, he hasn't.

No, she hasn't.

7 🖊️ **Look and write the names.**

I'm John.

I'm Emma.

I'm Robert.

I'm Julie.

1 _Emma_ has got a kitten.

2 _____ has got a lizard.

3 _____ has got a fish.

4 _____ hasn't got a pet.

Completing the sentences: writing

CLIL: What pets eat

8 ✏️ **Look, find and circle.**

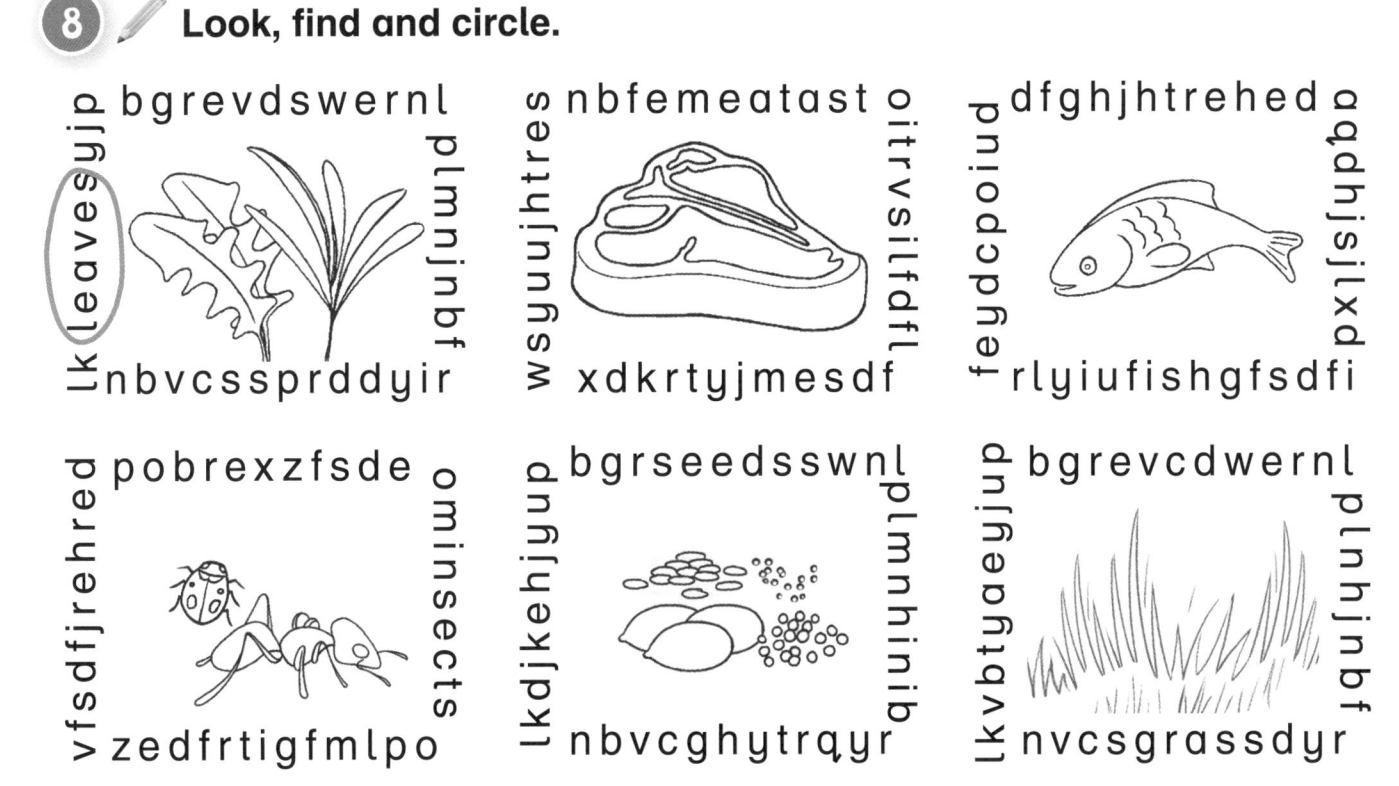

lkleavesyjp bgrevdswernl plmnjnbf
nbvcssprddyir

wsyuujhtres nbfemeatast oitrvsitfdfl
xdkrtyjmesdf

feydcpoiud dfghjhtrehed aqdhjsjlxd
rlyiufishgfsdfi

vfsdfjrehred pobrexzfsde ominsects
zedfrtigfmlpo

lkdjkehjyup bgrseedsswnl plmnhinib
nbvcghytrqyr

lkvbtyaeyjup bgrevcdwernl plnhjnbf
nvcsgrassdyr

9 **Look and count.** ✏️ **Write the number.**

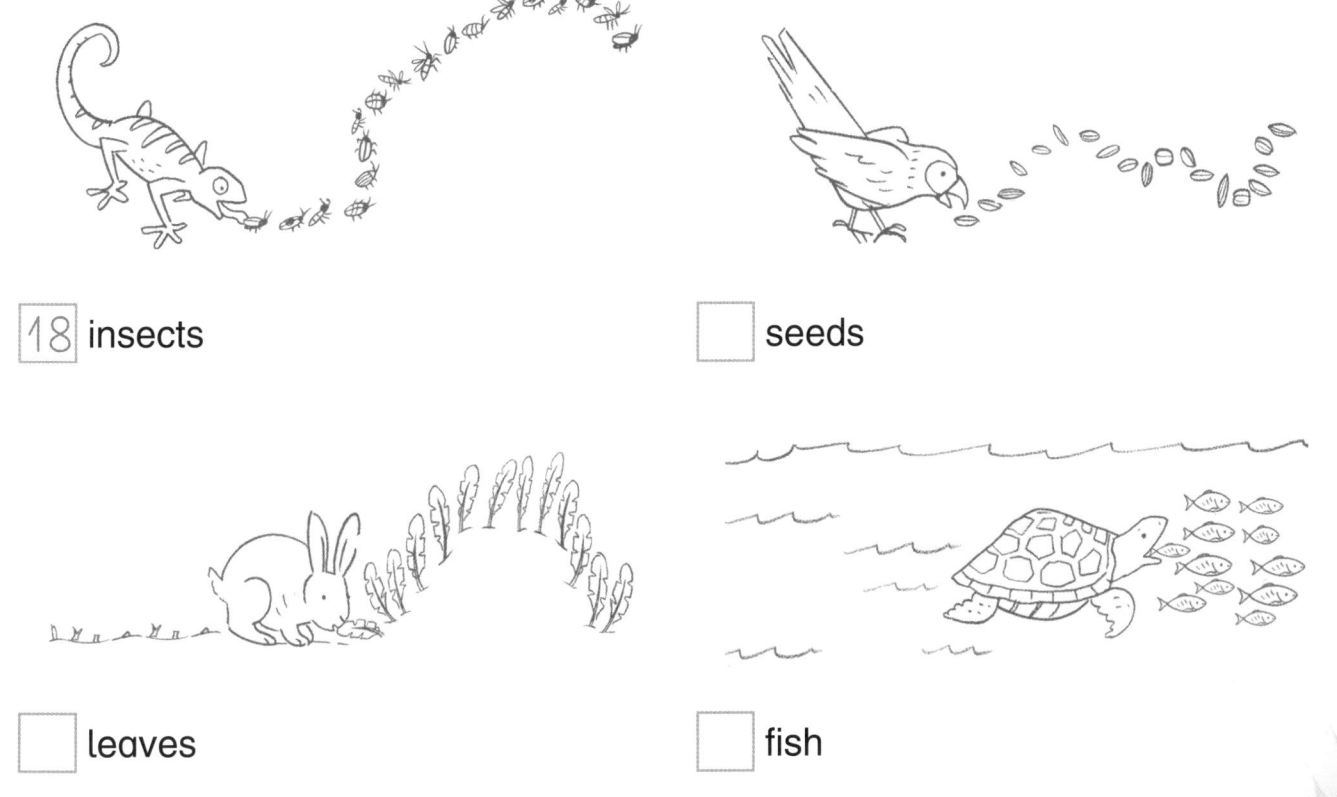

| 18 | insects |

| | seeds |

| | leaves |

| | fish |

Learning about content: reading

CLIL: What pets eat

10 ✏️ Write the animal and the food. 🖍️ Colour the paths.

seeds ~~meat~~ insects fish leaves

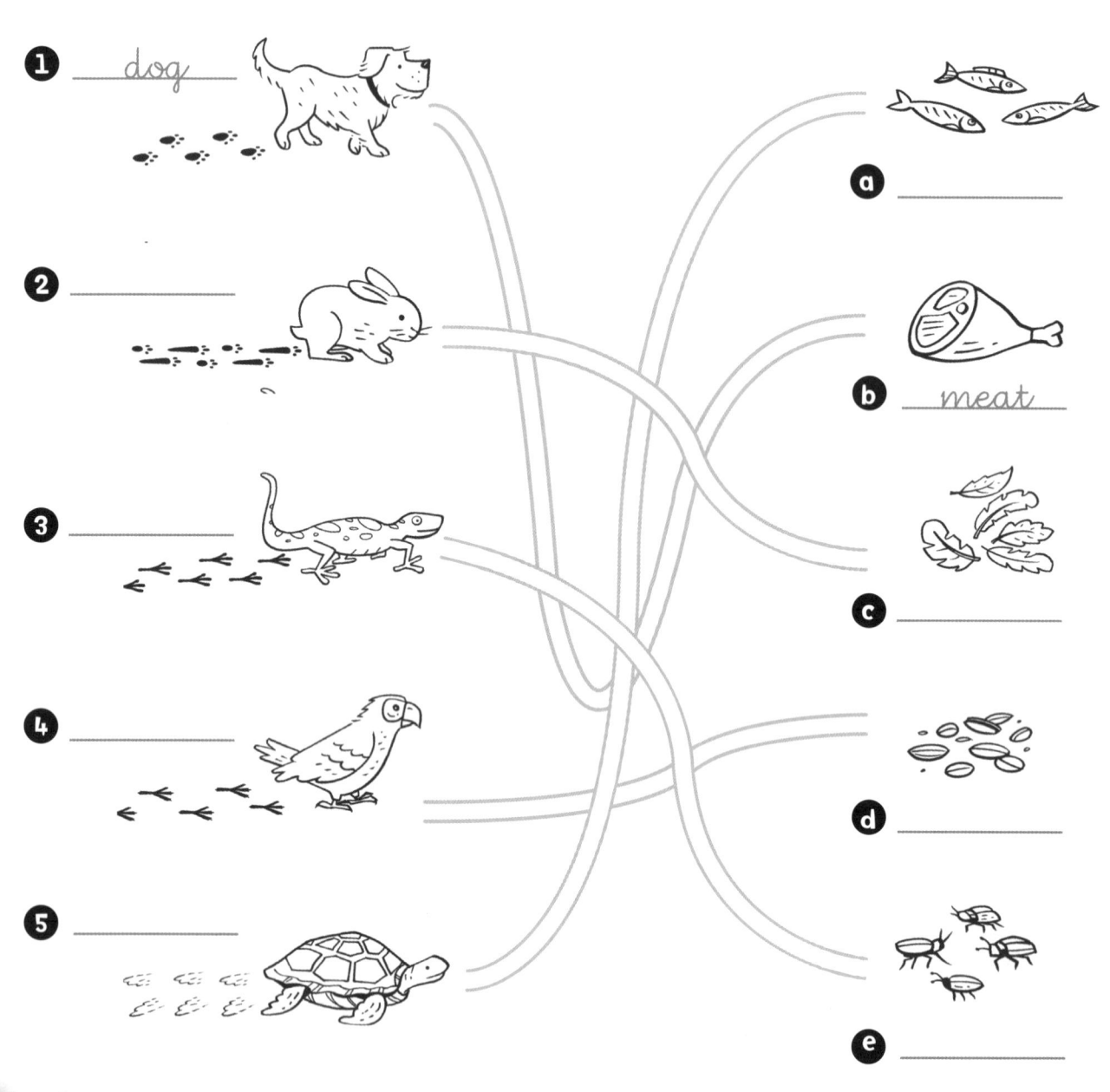

1 _dog_

2 _____

3 _____

4 _____

5 _____

a _____

b _meat_

c _____

d _____

e _____

11 ✏️ **Look at Activity 10 and write.**

1 Lizards eat ___insects___. **2** Dogs eat _____.

3 Parrots eat _____. **4** Rabbits eat _____.

5 Turtles eat _____.

Personalisation of content: writing

Unit review **Learning to LEARN**

12 ✏️ **Label the pictures. Complete the sentences.**

1

kitten

meat

Cats and ___kittens___
eat ___meat___ .

2

_____ eat

_____ .

3
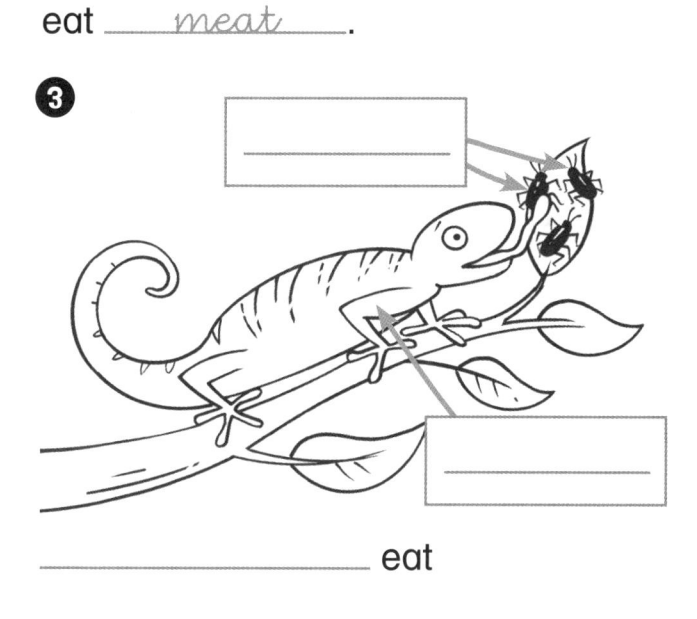

_____ eat

_____ .

4
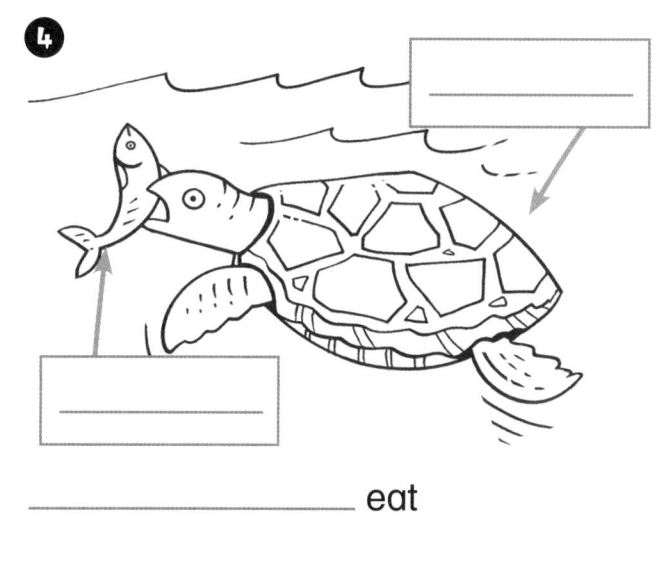

_____ eat

_____ .

13 ✏️ **Tick (✔) what you can do.**

1

rabbit

2

dog

3

4

Parrots eat seeds.

Dogs eat meat

Revision and self-assessment

Key for Activity 13: I can 1) say the names of pets, 2) read and write the names of pets, 3) understand the story, 4) read and write what pets eat.

Kids' Culture 2

1 CD1 45 🖊 **Listen and number in order.** 🎵 **Say the rhyme** *Two little dicky birds.*

☐ One named Peter,
one named Paul.

[1] Two little dicky birds,
sitting on a wall.

☐ Come back, Peter,
come back, Paul.

☐ Fly away, Peter,
fly away, Paul.

2 🖊 **Read and colour.**

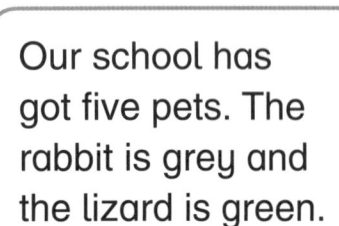

Our school has got five pets. The rabbit is grey and the lizard is green.

The guinea pig is brown and white. The parrot is red and blue, and the fish is orange.

Intercultural learning: reading and writing

Tiger Review 1

1 ✏️ **Look and write.**

turtle

living room

rabbit

hamster

kitchen

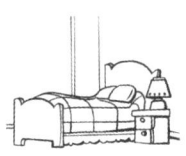

bedroom

bird

kitten

House rooms

living room

_____

_____

_____

_____

_____

_____

Animals

turtle

_____

_____

_____

_____

_____

_____

hall

dining room

garage

lizard

puppy

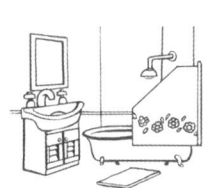

bathroom

fish

toilet

Units 1 and 2 revision

2 ✎ Look, read and write.

kitten shower pet hall insects garage

1 What has she got? Has she got a _kitten_?

2 Lizards eat leaves and _____.

3 The _____ is in the bathroom.

4 Where's Jay? Is he in the _____?

5 Where's Li? Is she in the _____?

6 Help! Tiger's got my new _____.

3 Where's my coat?

Vocabulary

1 ✏ **Read, look and number.** 💬 **Say.**

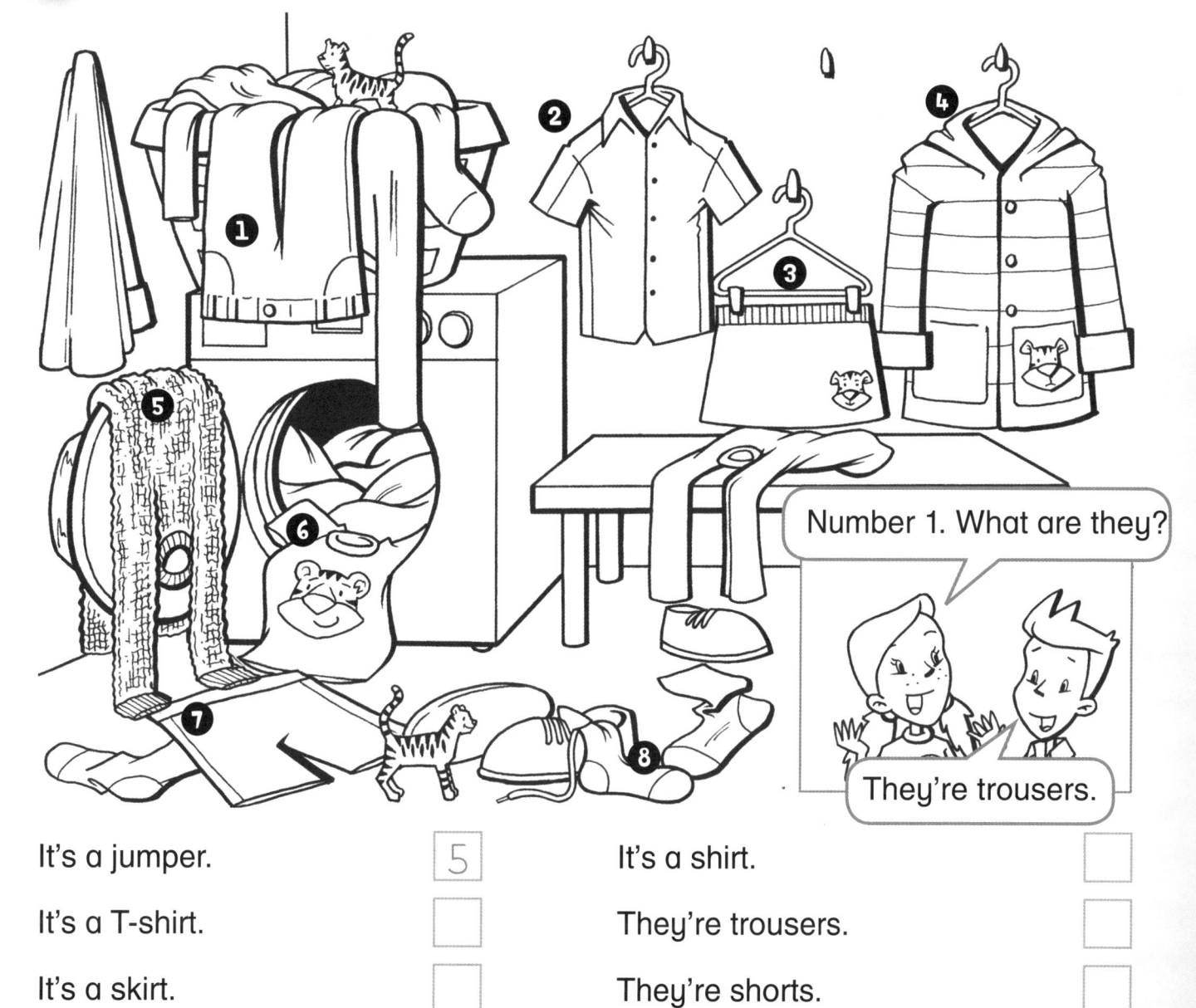

Number 1. What are they?

They're trousers.

It's a jumper.	5	It's a shirt.	
It's a T-shirt.		They're trousers.	
It's a skirt.		They're shorts.	
It's a coat.		They're shoes and socks.	

2 **Count the tigers.** ✏ **Write the number.**

 =

Vocabulary and story

3 ✏️ **Complete the dialogues.** 💬 **Act them out.**

shirt   T-shirt   ~~coat~~   jumper

1

Is this your _coat_?

No, it isn't. ☐

2

Is this your _____?

No, it isn't. ☐

3

Is this your _____?

Yes, it is. Thank you. ☐

4

Is this your _____?

No, it isn't. ☐

4 ✏️ **Tick (✔) the dialogues from the story in Activity 3.**

What do you think?

✏️ **Colour.**

The story is …

OK.

good.

great!

Story activity and vocabulary production: writing

Song

5 **Read and write.** **Listen and check.** 🎵 **Sing** *I'm wearing a coat.*

It's snowing today,

but I'm not cold.

No, I'm not cold.

I'm wearing a c*oat*_____.

Under the c_____,

I'm wearing a j_____,

and under the c_____,

I'm wearing s_____.

It's snowing today,

but I'm not cold.

No, I'm not cold.

I'm wearing a c_____, a j_____ and s_____.

I'm wearing a c_____, a j_____ and s_____.

I'm wearing a coat.

Recognising words in context: writing

Language and communication

6 ✏️ **Look, read and write.**

1

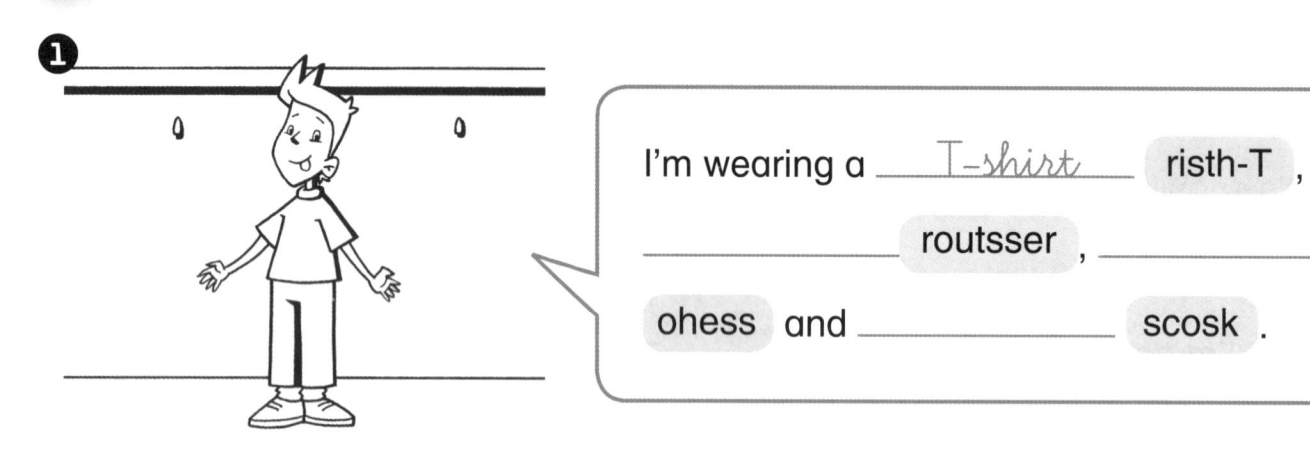

I'm wearing a ___T-shirt___ risth-T ,

_____ routsser , _____

ohess and _____ scosk .

2

I'm wearing a _____ risht

and a _____ skrit .

3

Tiger, you're wearing Sue's _____ toca .

You're wearing Li's _____ mujerp .

You're wearing Jay's _____ ohrsts .

7 ✏️ **Read and colour the illustrations in Activity 6.**

The skirt is purple.

The trousers are blue.

The T-shirt is yellow.

The shirt is pink.

The shoes and socks are brown and orange.

Completing the sentences: writing

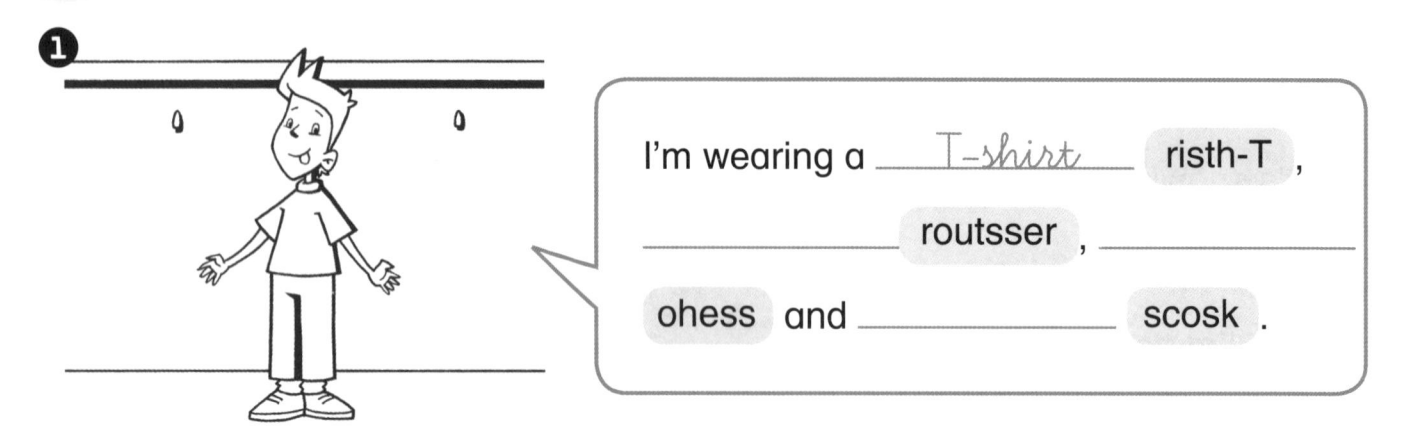

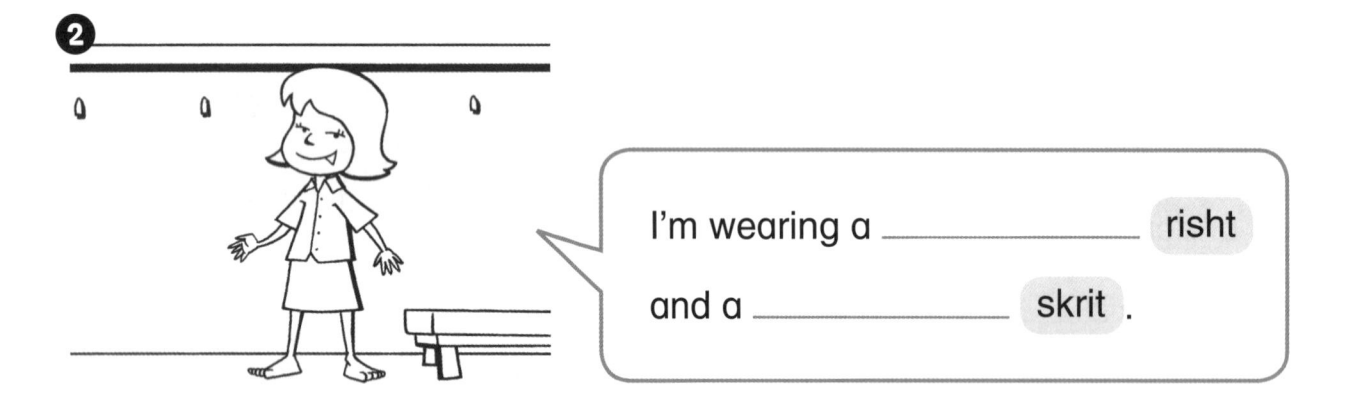

The T-shirt is yellow.

The shoes and socks are brown and orange.

The trousers are blue.

The shirt is pink.

Completing the sentences: writing

CLIL: Seasons and nature

8  Look, read and match. Colour the words.

1

a

spring

2

b

summer

3

c

autumn

4

d

winter

9  Draw your favourite season and write.

My favourite season is

_____.

CLIL: Seasons and nature

10 ✏️ Read and complete. 🔘 🎵 Check and sing *What's your favourite season?*

winter autumn summer spring

1

My favourite season is _spring_.
In _____,
you can see
flowers on the tree.

2

My favourite season is _____.
In _____,
you can see
fruit on the tree.

3

My favourite season is _____.
In _____,
you can see
leaves fall from the tree.

4

My favourite season is _____.
In _____,
you can see
snow on the tree.

Personalisation of content: writing

11 ✏️ **Look, read and write.**

> I'm wearing a ___coat___,
> _____ and _____.

> I'm _____
> _____.

❶

> My favourite season is
> _____.

❷

> My _____
> _____.

12 ✏️ **Tick (✔) what you can do.**

❶ jumper

❷ coat skirt shoes

❸

❹ winter spring summer

Revision and self-assessment

Key for Activity 12: I can 1) say the names of clothes, 2) read and write the names of clothes, 3) understand the story, 4) read and write the names of the seasons.

Kids' Culture 3

1 ✏️ **Number the lines in order.** ✏️ **Draw the snowman.**

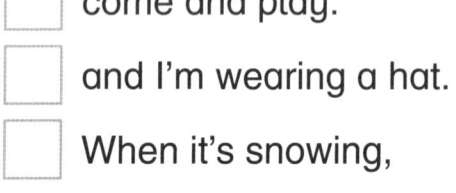

☐ I'm wearing a scarf

1 I'm a little snowman,

☐ come and play.

☐ and I'm wearing a hat.

☐ When it's snowing,

☐ hear me say,

☐ short and fat.

☐ come on children,

2 ✏️ **Look, read and match.**

a I live in Cardiff in the UK.
My favourite season is autumn. ☐ 3

b I live in London in the UK.
My favourite season is winter. ☐

c I live in Brighton in the UK.
My favourite season is summer. ☐

d I live in Edinburgh in the UK.
My favourite season is spring. ☐

Intercultural learning: reading and writing

 # Break Time

Vocabulary

1 ✏️ **Read, look and number.** 💬 **Say.**

☐ 4   It's football.

☐   It's tag.

☐   It's a computer game.

☐   It's cards.

☐   It's a board game.

☐   It's basketball.

☐   It's hopscotch.

☐   It's hide and seek.

Number 1. What's the game?

It's cards.

2 **Count the tigers.** ✏️ **Write the number.**

 = ☐

Vocabulary recognition: reading

Vocabulary and story

3 ✎ **Tick (✔) the five games in the story. Complete the sentence.**

board game ☐   hopscotch ✔   cards ☐   computer game ☐

football ☐   hide and seek ☐   tag ☐   basketball ☐

_____, _____

and _____ aren't in the story.

4 ✎ **Look and write.**

I want to play a *computer game*.

I want to play _____.

I want to play _____.

I want to play _____.

What do you think?

✎ **Colour.**

The story is …

OK.   good.   great!

Story activity and vocabulary production: reading and writing

Song

5 ✏ **Read and write.** 🎵 **Listen and check.** 🎵 **Sing** *I want to play.*

It's the break,

it's time to play.

What do you want to play today?

I want to play b*asketball*

and h_____ , too.

I want to play t_____ with you.

I want to play a c_____ g_____

and a b_____ g_____.

I want to play c_____ with you.

It's the break,

it's time to play.

What do you want to play today?

Let's play cards!

Yes, let's play cards!

Recognising words in context: writing

Language and communication

6 ✏️ **Complete the dialogues.** 💬 **Act them out.**

1

Do you want to play
basketball ?

No, thanks. I want to play _____.

2

Do you want to play _____?

No, thanks. I want to play a _____ _____.

3

Do you want to play a _____ _____?

Yes. Good idea! Let's play a _____ _____.

7 ✏️ **Order and write the sentences.**

1 | you | to | want | Do | play tag |

Do _____?

2 | thanks | No | want | play | to | I | football |

_____, _____. _____.

34

Completing the sentences: writing

CLIL: School rules

8 ✏ **Look, read and cross out the wrong words.**

Pong is in the canteen / ~~classroom~~.

Pong is in the playground / classroom.

Pong is in the classroom / corridor.

Pong is in the library / corridor.

Pong is in the gym / library.

Pong is in the canteen / playground.

9 ✏ **Look and match.**

You can't play computer games in the classroom.

You can't play ball games in the classroom.

Learning about content: reading

CLIL: School rules

10 ✏ **Find and circle.**

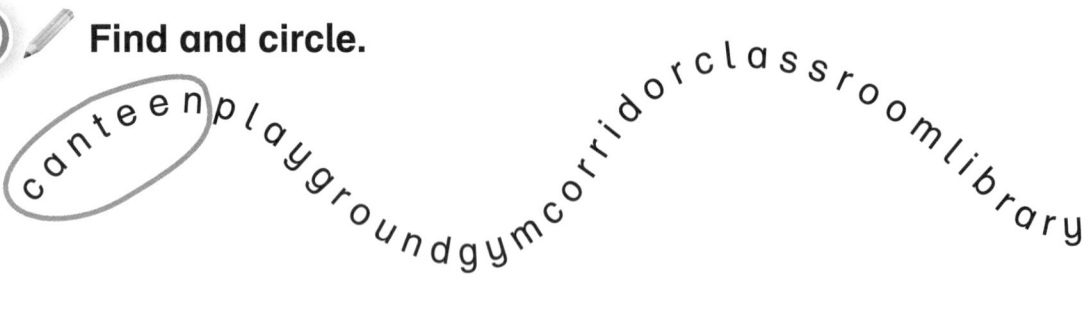

canteen playground gym corridor classroom library

11 ✏ **Write the names of the places. Read and match.**

playground _____ _____

You can't play
ball games
in the …

You can play
ball games
in the …

_____ _____ _____

Personalisation of content: writing

Unit review Learning to LEARN

12 ✏ **Label the pictures. Complete the sentences.**

cards

You can play cards in the classroom.

You _____ play _____ in the _____.

You _____ play ball games in the _____.

You _____ play ball games in the _____.

13 ✏ **Tick (✔) what you can do.**

1 basketball

2 board game tag *cards*

3

4 gym classr playgr *gym class*

Revision and self-assessment

Key for Activity 13: I can 1) say the names of games, 2) read and write the names of games, 3) understand the story, 4) read and write the names of places at school.

Kids' Culture 4

1 ✏️ 💬 **Write and say. Play** *Rock, paper, scissors.*

1

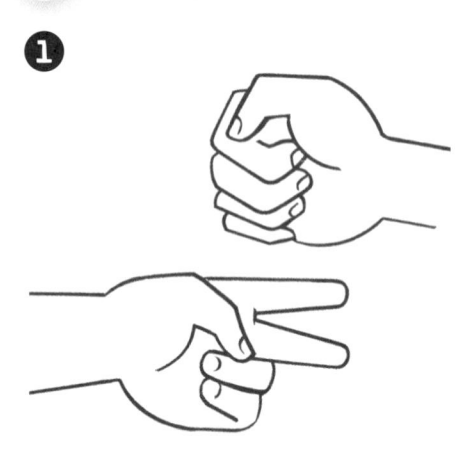

The winner is …

_____rock_____.

2

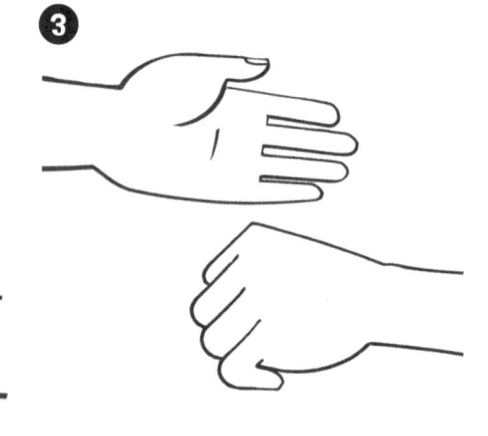

The winner is …

_____.

3

The winner is …

_____.

2 ✏️ **Look, read and match.**

1  **2**  **3**  **4**

We go to school in the UK.
At break time, we play football.

I play hide and seek with a friend.

I play tag with my friends.

I play cards in the classroom.

Intercultural learning: reading and writing

Tiger Review 2

1 ✏ **Look and write.**

football

coat

jumper

computer game

hide and seek

T-shirt

tag

Clothes

coat

_____

_____

_____

_____

_____

_____

_____

Games

football

_____

_____

_____

_____

_____

_____

_____

hopscotch

board game

skirt

cards

shoes and socks

shirt

trousers

shorts

basketball

2 🖊️ **Read and write.**

shorts   ~~season~~   basketball   classroom   board game   coat

1 My favourite _season_ is winter.

2 Tiger, you're wearing my _____!

3 I want to play _____.

4 Pong, stop! You can't play ball games in the _____.

5 Do you want to play a _____, Tiger?

6 I'm wearing a _____, a jumper and shorts.

5 What's the matter?

Vocabulary

1 ✏️ **Read and write the number.** 💬 **Say.**

Number 1.
What's he got?

He's got a cough.

❶ He's got a cough.

❷ He's got a headache.

❸ He's got a cut.

❹ He's got tummy ache.

❺ She's got toothache.

❻ She's got earache.

❼ She's got a cold.

❽ She's got a sore throat.

2 **Count the tigers.** ✏️ **Write the number.**

 = ☐

41

Vocabulary and story

3 🖉 **Tick (✔) the health problems in the story.**

cough ✔ tummy ache ☐ sore throat ☐ cut ☐

earache ☐ toothache ☐ cold ☐ headache ☐

4 🖉 **Look and write.**

1 I've got a
headache.

2 I've got
_____.

3 I've got a
_____.

4 I've got a
_____.

What do you think?

🖉 **Colour.**

The story is …

 OK.  good.  great!

Story activity and vocabulary production: writing

Song

5 CD3 9 ✏ **Listen, read and complete.** 🎵 **Sing *I'm feeling ill.***

What's the matter?

How are you today?

I'm feeling ill,

so I can't play.

I can't go to school for two or three days.

I've got a ___*sore*___ roes throat,

and a bad _____ coguh ,

a sore _____ trhota ,

and a bad, bad _____ gucoh .

I've got a _____ hehacdae ,

and a bad _____ clod ,

a _____ hdaceahe ,

and a bad, bad _____ dolc .

Recognising words in context: writing

Language and communication

6 ✏️ **Complete the dialogues.** 💬 **Act them out.**

1
Have you _got_ toothache?

Yes , I have.

2
_____ you _____ earache?

_____, I haven't.

3
_____ you _____ a headache?

_____, _____
_____.

7 ✏️ **Order and write the sentences.**

1 feeling | I'm | ill

_____.

2 cold | you | Have | got | a

_____?

3 I | No | haven't | earache | got | I've

_____, _____. _____.

44

Completing the sentences: writing

CLIL: Keeping healthy

8 ✏️ **Look and match.**

eat well

drink water

do exercise

play

sleep well

wash

9 ✏️ **Look at Activity 8 and number the sentences.**

I play basketball.	4	I eat apples.	
I have a shower.		I go to bed early.	
I ride a bike.		I wash my hands.	

CLIL: Keeping healthy

10 ✏️ **Write and match.**

do exercise   drink water   eat well   play   sleep well   ~~wash~~

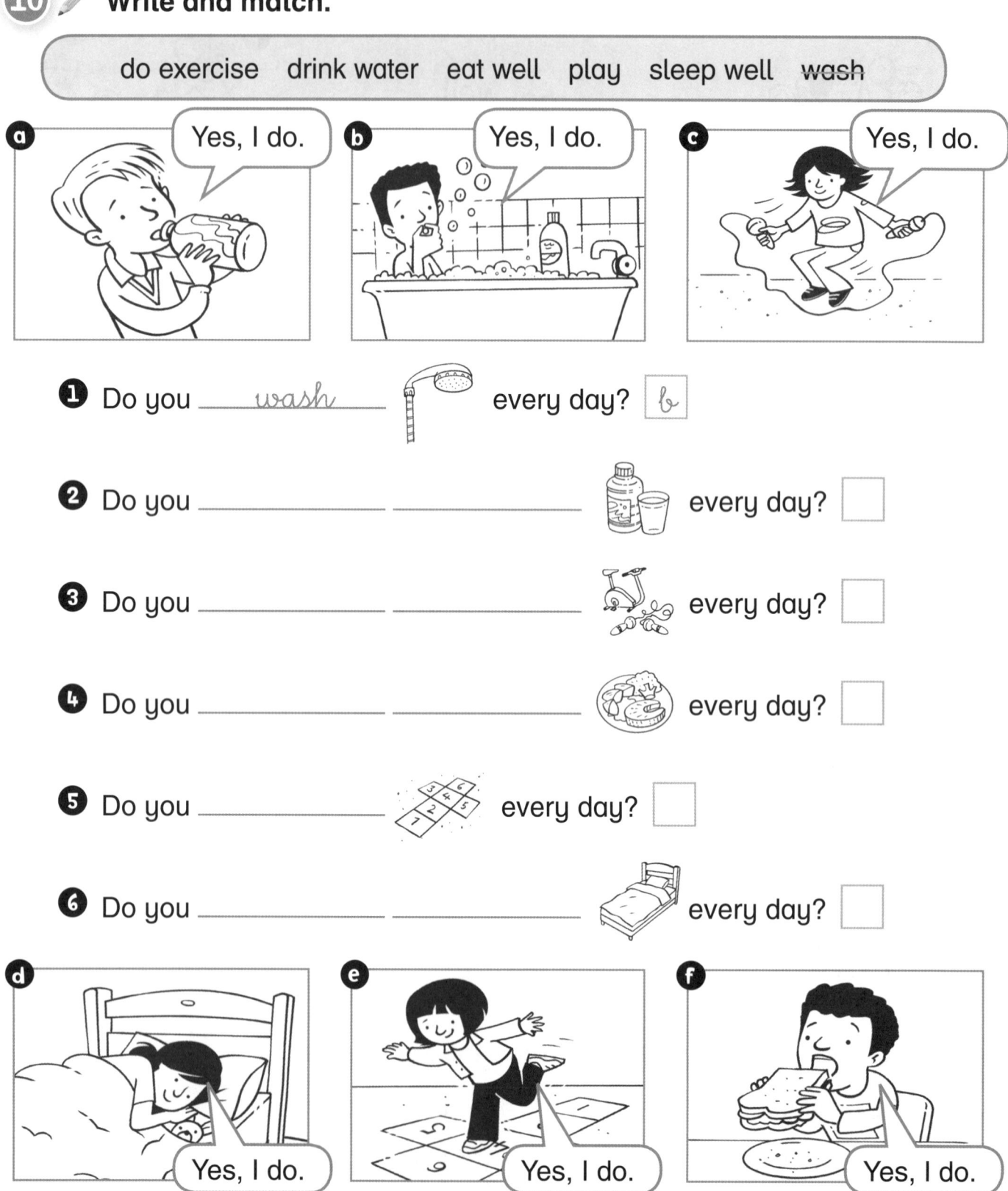

1 Do you ___wash___ 🚿 every day? *b*

2 Do you _____ _____ every day? ☐

3 Do you _____ _____ every day? ☐

4 Do you _____ _____ every day? ☐

5 Do you _____ every day? ☐

6 Do you _____ _____ every day? ☐

11 💬 **Ask and answer for you.**

46

Personalisation of content: writing

12 🖊 **Look, read and write.**

I _____ _do_ _____ exercise and I _____ water.

I _____ well.

I'm feeling ill.
I've got a _____
_____.

I'm feeling ill.
I've got _____
_____.

13 🖊 **Tick (✓) what you can do.**

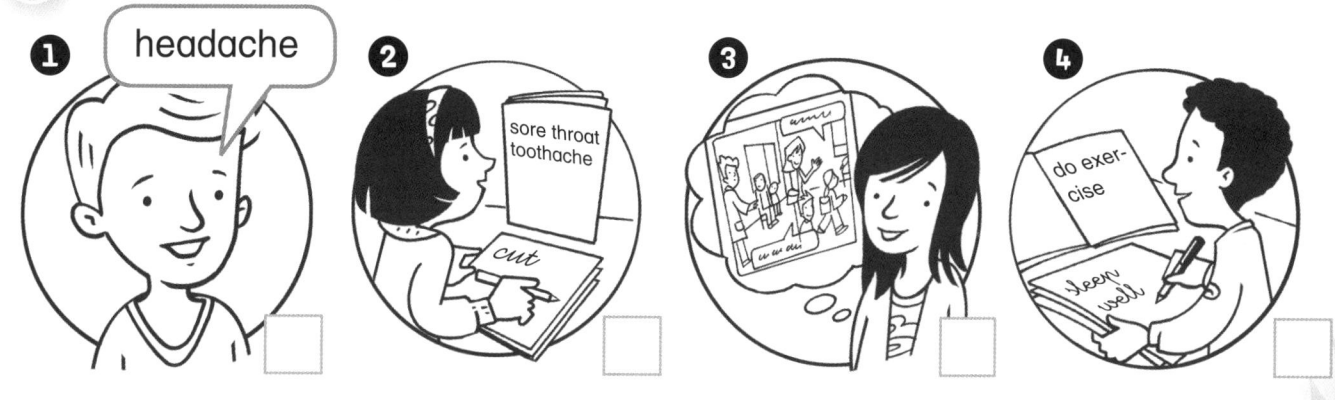

1 headache

2 sore throat toothache · cut

3

4 do exer-cise · keep well

Revision and self-assessment   **Key for Activity 13:** I can 1) say the names of health problems, 2) read and write the names of health problems, 3) understand the story, 4) read and write ways of keeping healthy.

Kids' Culture 5

1 🖋 **Look and write.** 💬 **Read and act out the joke.**

> leg ~~foot~~ finger nose arm

Doctor, doctor!

When I touch my ___*foot*___ 🦶, it hurts.

When I touch my _____ 🦵, it hurts.

When I touch my _____ 💪, it hurts.

When I touch my _____ 👃, it hurts.

Doctor, what's the matter with me?

Hmm. You've got a broken _____ .

2 🖋 **Look, read and match.**

I sleep well. 4

I eat well. ☐

I do exercise. ☐

I play. ☐

Intercultural learning: reading and writing

 # On Holiday

Vocabulary

1 ✏️ **Read and write the number.** 💬 **Say.**

5

1 It's an ice rink.

2 It's a park.

3 It's a swimming pool.

4 It's a zoo.

5 It's a funfair.

6 It's a water park.

7 It's a beach.

8 It's an aquarium.

Number 1. What is it?

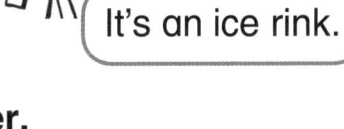

It's an ice rink.

2 **Count the tigers.** ✏️ **Write the number.**

 = ☐

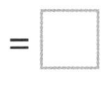

Vocabulary recognition: reading

Vocabulary and story

3 🖍 **Tick (✔) where Tiger wants to go.**

park ☐ aquarium ☐ beach ☐ water park ☐

zoo ☐ ice rink ☐ funfair ☐ swimming pool ☐

4 🖍 **Look and write.**

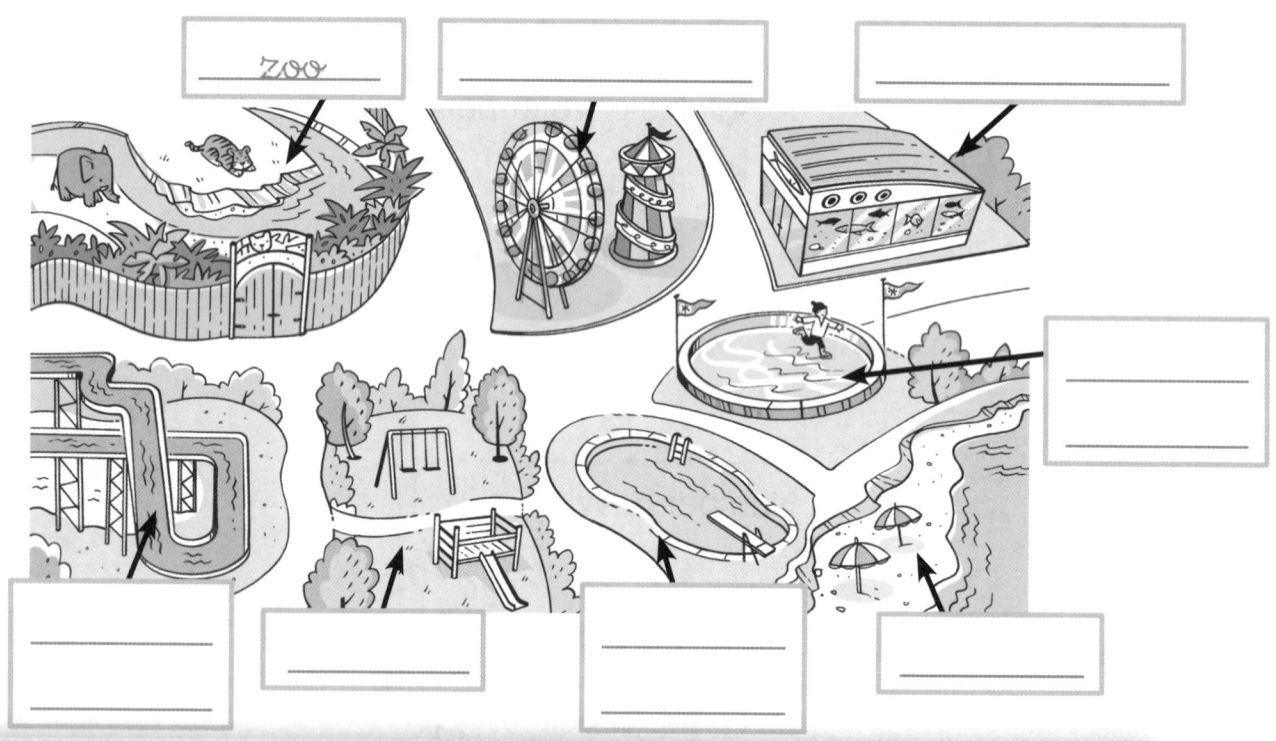

zoo

What do you think?

🖍 **Colour.**

The story is …

 OK.

 good.

 great!

Story activity and vocabulary production: writing

Song

5 Listen, read and complete. ♫ Sing *In this town*.

In this town,

there's a lot to do.

There's an ___*ice*___ ___*rink*___ iec nrik ,

and a _____ ozo .

There's a very long _____ bceah ,

a _____ _____ smwigmin loop ,

and a _____ ffunair , too!

Let's go to the funfair!

In this town,

there's a lot to do.

There's a _____ _____

waetr arpk ,

and a _____ ozo .

There's a very big _____ pkar ,

an _____ aqriuuam ,

and a _____ ffunair , too!

Let's go to the funfair!

Recognising words in context: writing

Language and communication

6 ✏️ **Complete the dialogues.** 💬 **Act them out.**

1

Is there a zoo?

Yes, there is.

2

____ ____ a swimming pool?

_____, there isn't.

3

____ ____ a beach?

Yes, ____
____.

7 ✏️ **Read and draw the town.**

There's a zoo.

There's a beach.

There's a park.

There's an aquarium.

There's a water park.

There's a funfair.

Completing the sentences: writing

CLIL: Road safety

8 ✏️ **Find and circle 10 differences.** 💬 **Say.**

Stand on the pavement.

AQUARIUM

Park

Don't cross the road!

15

Water Park and Ice Rink

Look left and right.

Stand on the pavement.

ZOO

Swimming Pool

Don't cross the road!

14

Water Park and Funfair

Look left and right.

9 **Look at Activity 8.** ✏️ **Circle the place that's missing.**

park	water park	aquarium	funfair
swimming pool	beach	zoo	ice rink

CLIL: Road safety

 **Look and tick (✔) or cross (✗). Write.**

Stand on the pavement.   Cross the road.   Look left and right.

1  ✔  ✗

Stand on the pavement.

2

_____

3

_____

Personalisation of content: writing

6

Unit review Learning to LEARN

11 🖊 **Label the pictures. Complete the sentences.**

swimming pool

Stand on the pavement.

Look _____ .

_____

12 🖊 **Tick (✔) what you can do.**

1 funfair

2 zoo aquarium / park

3

4 stop look left / look right

Revision and self-assessment

Key for Activity 12: I can 1) say the names of places, 2) read and write the names of places, 3) understand the story, 4) read and write road safety rules.

Kids' Culture 6

1 ✏️ **Number the lines in order.** 🎧 **Listen and check.**

☐ to see what he can see, see, see.

☐ But all that he can see, see, see,

☑ 1 ☑ A sailor goes to sea, sea, sea,

☐ is the bottom of the deep blue sea, sea, sea.

2 ✏️ **Read and match.**

1 I go to the swimming pool every week.

2 I go to the cinema every week.

3 I play with my friends in the park after school.

 a

 b

 c

Intercultural learning: reading and writing

Tiger Review 3

1 ✏️ **Look and write.**

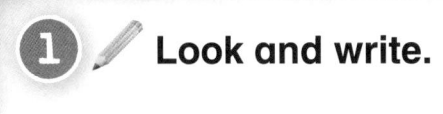
cough

funfair

earache

ice rink

water park

park

headache

aquarium

Health problems

cough

_____

_____

_____

_____

_____

_____

_____

Places

funfair

_____

_____

_____

_____

_____

_____

_____

swimming pool

sore throat

zoo

cut

tummy ache

cold

beach

toothache

Read and write.

ice rink   pavement   ~~drink~~   lion   tummy ache   feeling

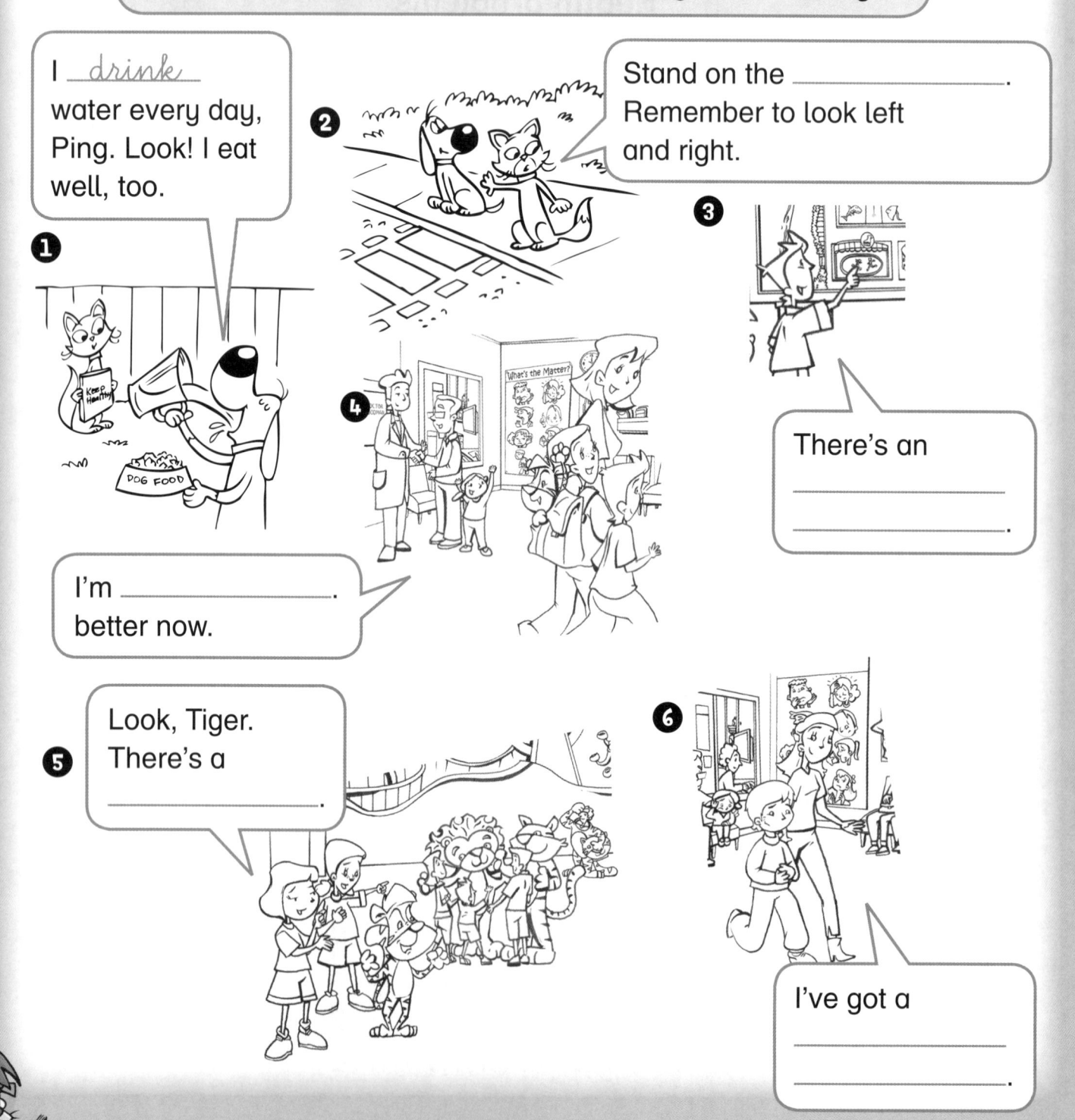

1 I _drink_ water every day, Ping. Look! I eat well, too.

2 Stand on the _____. Remember to look left and right.

3 There's an _____ _____.

4 I'm _____. better now.

5 Look, Tiger. There's a _____.

6 I've got a _____ _____.

Festivals

Halloween

1 ✏️ **Look, find and circle the words. Write.**

mjutlsashcsskeletonalpqwmikl (monster)kjhytrbgtrdswertyuioinspidermnhgtuiolzbvhgfdsxib lpqwebtvbmoonksdgeecxalpit

m o n s t e r

s _ _ _ _ _ _ _

m _ _ _ _

s _ _ _ _ _ _

w _ _ _ _ _ _

zopthwerbnmkhiucferwswizardlpterdopbyuinqsdfaflceruipiy

2 ✏️ **Complete the dialogue.** 💬 **Act it out.**

Halloween   box   ~~surprise~~   What   spider

I've got a _____surprise_____ for you.

_____ is it?

Look in the _____.

It's a _____. Yuk!

Happy _____!

Christmas

1 ✏️ **Look, read and write.**

| sawnflkeo | ahitCrsms stiokncg | Chmristas crad | aFtehr thris-maCs | Cmahrists ckae |

snowflake _____ _____ _____ _____

2 ✏️ **Complete the dialogue.** 💬 **Act it out.**

~~Christmas~~   snowflake   Thank   card   picture

Happy _Christmas_ !

_____ you. Look! I've got a Christmas _____.

What's the _____?

It's a _____.

Vocabulary input

Carnival

1 Do the crossword.

Down ↓

1 

3 

Across →

2 

3 

4 

2 Complete the dialogue. Act it out.

~~Hello~~ pirate wearing What Welcome

Hello !

Hi! ________________ to the party!

I'm ________________ fancy dress. ________________ am I? Can you guess?

You're a ________________.

CLIL Picture Dictionary

Unit 1

bed

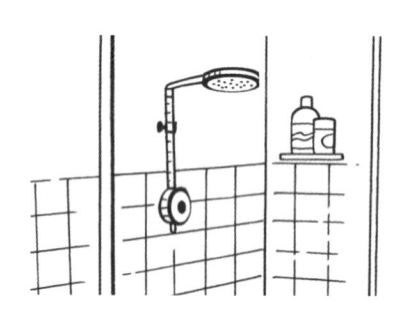

Unit 2

leaves

Unit 3

spring

_____ _____

_____ _____ _____

Unit 4

classroom

_____ _____

_____ _____ _____

Unit 5

drink water

Unit 6

Stop!